FRED BASSET

by ALEX GRAHAM

Chapmans Publishers Ltd
141-143 Drury Lane
London WC2B 5TB

First Published by Chapmans 1992

© Associated Newspapers Ltd 1992

ISBN 1 85592 732 2

Printed in England by
Clays Ltd, St Ives plc

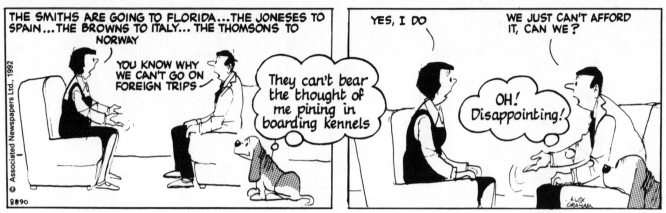

What's the world coming to?

Sparrows never used to behave like this!

You can never tell with Jock! One moment he's in one of his black moods...

Then, all of a sudden, he throws it off...

...and he's back to his usual cheerful, chirpy self

Your newspaper, Sir

THANK YOU, FRED

8847

Watch this! I pass it to him immaculately folded...

...and no sooner does he get his hands on to it than he has it in a complete mess!

ALEX GRAHAM

© Associated Newspapers Ltd., 1992

That makes a change

8848

For once, he didn't slice into the pond

He hooked into the undergrowth

© Associated Newspapers Ltd., 1992

HEEL, FRED!

The art of appearing to obey **WITHOUT ACTUALLY DOING SO!**

© Associated Newspapers Ltd., 1992

8825

We can be walking along quite normally...

© Associated Newspapers Ltd., 1992

...when suddenly Jock will launch himself into his famous backward somersault

That means he's feeling good

8820

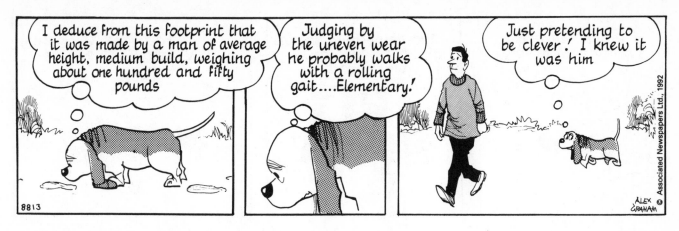

'HAD TO GO OUT. GIVE FRED HIS DINNER. I'VE MADE IT UP AND IT'S IN THE FRIDGE'

Good!

'P.S. BOIL YOURSELF AN EGG OR SOMETHING

8756

There are times when she's lacking in tact

It's eerie!

8757

Nobody there!

Why do the stairs always creak when they're out and I'm here on my own?

ANY SUGGESTIONS FOR SUPPER?

HOW ABOUT POULET EN COCOTTE BON FEMME?

VERY FUNNY, I'M SURE! MACARONI CHEESE

He will have his little joke

8752

They're not even warm

8753

We often play this game. Hunt the slipper

WHERE HAVE YOU PUT IT?

Behind the refrigerator, actually

ALEX GRAHAM